PARENTS, ZITS AND HAIRY BITS: The World According to Wilf

by
Gez Walsh

𝔗𝔥𝔢 𝔎𝔦𝔫𝔤'𝔰 𝔈𝔫𝔤𝔩𝔞𝔫𝔡 𝔓𝔯𝔢𝔰𝔰
2000

ISBN 1 872438 46 6

Parents, Zits and Hairy Bits is typeset by Moose Manuscripts
in Baskerville 14pt and published by
The King's England PressLtd,
Cambertown House, Commercial Road, Goldthorpe,
Rotherham, South Yorkshire, S63 9BL

Printed and bound in Great Britain by

Woolnough Bookbinding
Irthlingborough
Northamptonshire

FOREWORD

He's back! Wilf, hero of *The Spot on My Bum*, *The Return of the Spot* and *The Man in The Skirt*, returns in this new collection of rude poems.

Wilf is now thirteen and his body is starting to change. Things are different for him now. He knows so much more than before, but his parents seem to be getting more stupid.

In this collection, Wilf looks back at when he was younger and at his life now. But, as usual, there are also poems which have nothing to do with him.

So, for those of you who are not yet thirteen, this is what's to come. For those of you who *are* thirteen: ha, ha, ha! And to all those people out there who, like me, are well past their "sell by" date, take that smug grin off your face!

Dedications

To Lee, for being thirteen and passing on all your great knowledge and wisdom to me and for curing my stupidity.
Carol - don't worry! It can only last a year... can't it?!

Thank Yous

Thanks to Steve Rudd for backing me on the last poem in *Someone's Nicked My Knickers*.
Thanks to Debbie Nunn for editing my books.
Thanks to Phill... (Debbie's editing again! Only kidding!!) to Phil Rendell, the human worker bee.

Teenager

Now that my brother's a teenager
He has turned into a bore,
And he's now growing hairs
Where he didn't have them before.

He has lost the power of speech,
He now acts like a spoilt brat;
Mum says it's just a phase
And I'll end up like that.

His body is now changing,
His emotions are all in knots,
His voice goes up and down
And his face is covered in spots.

He says that we don't understand
And that we no longer care.
He says he's now a young man
With spots and fluffy facial hair.

He wants a place of his own,
Dad says it's just a dream,
Because it's hard to get a house
When you're only thirteen!

Wilf's Guide To Life

When life is difficult,
The going gets tough;
When people are at you
And you're feeling rough
Don't worry, all will be fine,
Just you wait and see,
When you say these words:
IT WASN'T ME!

Young Man From Crete

There was a young man from Crete,
Who had to take a seat.
He felt so queasy,
Something smelled cheesy,
Then realised it was his feet.

The Blister

I got a blister on my finger
When I pricked it on a rose;
I hope it heals up very soon
Because it stops me from picking my nose.

Brace Yourself For The News

Something strange is happening,
There's something going wrong;
I've just had a new brace fitted
And it's started to pick up Radio One.

My mouth it vibrates,
My teeth start to tingle;
I then give the news
As my brace picks up a signal.

The dentist is baffled,
He's never known this before;
He's altered my brace
But now I receive Radio Four!

Having A Bad Time?

My sister took a note
To her teacher today;
Excuse her from swimming
Is what it had to say.
Mum had written the note,
My sister was still in bed.
The note had stated
She was having a bad period.
This really got me angry;
My sister lay there grinning.
I've had lots of bad periods
But I didn't get off swimming!
Can you remember that time
My little hamster went and died?
For me that was a bad period,
I just sat and cried and cried.
Mum then tried to explain
That because I am a boy
I will never have a period,
And for that I should jump for joy.
But I think it's so unfair,
I think it's so unjust.
I am going to start a campaign,
I think that I must.
Boys and girls are equal,
Right is on my side;

My sister's bad period is no worse
Then when my little hamster died.
So come on friends,
Make a lot of noise;
Fair play for everyone,
And bad periods for boys.

My Friend's Mum

My friend's mum is big and hairy,
She has tattoos on her arms
And is called Bloody Mary.
She rides a big motor bike
In her studded leather jacket;
The bike has no exhaust
So it makes such a racket.
Her new boyfriend's called Jack;
He has 'death' tattooed on his head
And 'I love mum' on his back.
They look so fearsome when they're together
With their tattoos and chains
And dressed all in black leather.
What has made these two strange creatures?
It must be their work:
They're both supply teachers!

Timmy's Ten Pound Turd

Come on kids, have you heard?
Timothy's found a ten pound turd.
He found it by a circus tent,
The previous owner was an elephant.
He took it to school in a box,
The smell blew off Miss Parker's socks.
She wanted to know from where
This strange object had come;
Timothy thought for a moment
Then replied, "From a giant bum."
She pushed it away in horror;
"Why have you brought this to me?"
Timothy put the box on the nature table
Then declared, "It's for all to see!"
Miss Parker, with hand over mouth, said,
"Just take it away very quickly,
It's filling the room with flies
And making me feel quite sickly."
So with a heavy heart Timmy
Picked up his pile of dung,
The class rose to their feet
And clapped and cheered one by one.
They held their breath
Then they held their noses,
The caretaker came and took it

To spread over his roses.
So the next time your teacher
Asks those that are able
To bring something strange
For the new nature table
Think big, not boring,
Don't be such a nerd;
Be like our hero, Timmy,
And bring in a ten pound turd.

Young Man From Augusta

There was a young man from Augusta
Who was feeling quite lacklustre;
So just for a thrill
He swallowed a pill
And grew a pair of busters.

I Will Never Be A...

When I grow up I want to be
A navy captain going out to sea,
Or an astronaut flying to the moon,
A photographer in a darkened room,
A brickie, a joiner, a sparkie, a miner,
Zookeeper, road sweeper, harvest reaper
A bailer, a tailor, government gaoler,
A vendor, a spender, even a money-lender.
I could be a matchmaker, act like Cupid,
But I'll never be a teacher, I'm not that stupid!

Spots!

Oh, no! I'm getting spots!
Turning into a greaser.
My body's like a moon shot,
My face is like a pizza.

I don't know how I got them,
Or if they'll ever stop,
But every time I smile
Another one goes pop!

I've tried on many lotions,
Tablets, swabs and creams,
But they keep on getting bigger
Till they pop like custard screams.

It must be some sort of plague
With an unusual sort of name
Because all my friends my age
Have them, just the blinkin' same.

Big, Bad Goldilocks!

There was a girl named Goldilocks
Who one day, while out walking,
Came upon three big bears
That she'd recently been stalking.
She decided on a spot of burglary
At their humble little cottage,
Climbed in through a window
And ate up all their porridge.
This common thief felt tired,
Being so over-fed,
So she crawled up the stairs
And crashed out on the bed.
When the bears arrived home,
All aching for some food,
Someone had scoffed all their grub
Putting them in such a violent mood.
They all sneaked up the stairs
And found Goldilocks a-sleeping,
So they all took it in turns
To kick her gleaming teeth in.

Money-bags?

Grandad's got a sore bum,
He's not feeling very well.
I know he tries to hide it,
But I can always tell.

His problem is his money,
He says as he smiles.
He must have a lot,
He says that he has piles!

I Want To Go To The Dentist!

I'm going to the dentist
And I really don't care.
He can drill where he likes,
Stick fillings anywhere.
The reason I'm not bothered
When I'd usually be feeling glum
Is that I'm taking my little sister;
I'm not having anything done!

Are Vampires Real?

We watched a film tonight,
No one knows how I feel;
But I must ask one question:
Do you think vampires are real?

My mum and dad say 'no',
But I'm not so sure;
And what if one bit you?
Is there any known cure?

I know that I'm being stupid,
I've never even seen a vampire's mark;
But I would make a useless vampire
Because I'm so scared of the dark.

Bad Lad Dad!

My teacher was telling me
That he had taught my dad too.
He said, "You're not a bad lad,
"Your dad was much worse than you!"

Camp Horrid

Last year we went on holiday
And stayed out in a tent;
My dad thinks we enjoyed it
But we wished we never went.

Sleeping out in a freezing field
With just canvas for a cover
Might be good for the S.A.S.
But not for me, a comfort-lover.

Dad said, "We're back to nature!"
He felt he was nature's child.
Have you tried going to the toilet
When you're living in the wild?

Dad said, "Hide in the bushes,
You will soon find it such fun."
I'd no sooner pulled my pants down
When a nettle stung my bum.

Then there was our washing
Which we did in a local stream.
Upon some rocks I washed my socks
When a moo cow made me scream.

It had sneaked up beside me
Then licked me on the ear;
It didn't half remind me
Of a girl I snogged last year.

Finally there was the cooking,
Which we did on an open fire.
Charred black meat and tea so sweet
It really tasted quite dire.

Dad says he just can't wait
For us to do it all again.
We hope that he enjoys it because
We're sneaking off to Spain!

Our Perry's Poohed His Pants!

I will tell you a story
About my big brother, Perry:
He had an accident
And moved in a hurry.
It was the other evening
When Perry and me
Had settled to watch
A programme on tv.
Perry was showing off,
The way big brothers do,
When he let off a fart
Then followed through.
He jumped in the air
Holding on to his bum.
I asked, "What's wrong, Perry?
"What have you done?"
His face was filled with horror,
He did a strange dance;
Then I smelled his problem:
Our Perry had poohed his pants!
He ran for the door,
He needed the loo,
He held on so tight
To his pants filled with pooh.
I then shouted out, "Mum!"
Perry gave a worried glance

As I shouted and screamed:
"Our Perry's poohed his pants!"
Perry couldn't stop me
As I let out that shout,
His hands clamped to his pants
In case anything fell out.
He ran like a turkey,
A very strange gait;
"Our Perry's poohed his pants!"
Must be something he ate.
Mum was very angry,
I started to laugh;
Perry took his pants off
And climbed into the bath.
Mum banged on the door,
"What's wrong with you?
If you want to fart
You should go to the loo!"
So Perry cleaned up
Then threatened me grief;
If I told anyone
I would lose most of my teeth.
So I gave him my word,
My mouth is shut tight,
But it's going to be fun
When his girlfriend calls tonight!

Parents

Parents are so stupid,
Parents are so daft.
They are so boring,
Kids like a good laugh.

Parents just don't know
What fun is all about.
They whine and they moan,
They scream and they shout.

They say, "Do this!"
They say, "Do that!
Clean up that mess.
Don't sit on the cat!"

So this is what you must do
To cut out all their rage:
Get them both trained
From a very early age.

The Day We Went To The Zoo

Miss Evans and Miss Zola
Were acting like Noah
Lining us up two by two,
The day we went to the zoo.

The teachers were smoking,
The children were choking
While screaming for the loo,
The day we went to the zoo.

At last we arrived,
Keen to get inside,
Pushing our way through,
The day we went to the zoo

Claire Pollard was crying,
Really, I'm not lying!
She was bawling out "boo hoo",
The day we went to the zoo.

Miss Henry asked, "Why?
What's making you cry?"
Claire said, "It's down to. you!"
The day we went to the zoo.

Then she called her a hag,
Said, "You didn't load my bag
Which I'd left in full view,"
The day we went to the zoo.

But we were having such fun,
Found a pile of elephant dung
Which we slung at little Drew,
The day we went to the zoo.

Then the monkeys we teased,
They weren't very pleased
As they pelted us with their pooh,
The day we went to the zoo.

Then Miss Zola got vexed
As the zebras had sex,
She tried to cover up our view,
The day we went to the zoo.

Then Mr Dempster and Miss Lyle
Went missing for a while
But were found by little Drew,
The day we went to the zoo.

They were found behind a log
Having a passionate snog
And getting themselves in a stew,
The day we went to the zoo.

They got the fright of their life
Because Mr Dempster has a wife
And she'd kill him if she knew,
The day we went to the zoo.

Then it was time to go home,
We started to curse and moan
Turning the air quite blue,
The day we went to the zoo.

We all got back on the bus
With one heck of a fuss
But we were missing one or two,
The day we went to the zoo.

The bus set off so quick
That a few children were sick
And a few of the teachers too,
The day we went to the zoo.

Then came a bad smell,
From where we couldn't tell
But we all called out "phew!"
The day we went to the zoo.

We traced back the smell
To old Mrs McTell
Who had drunk a strange brew,
The day we went to the zoo.

She had got herself drunk,
Then stolen a skunk
And given it the name Lou,
The day we went to the zoo.

Then the bus broke down.
Said the driver, with a frown,
"I've had enough of your crew!"
The day we went to the zoo.

Then he announced with a cough,
"Right, that's it, I'm off."
Said Miss Evans, "I'm coming too!"
The day we went to the zoo.

So we phoned Mrs Bell,
The head teacher from hell
With the face of a kangaroo,
The day we went to the zoo.

She got us all back
Then gave Mr Dempster the sack
Because of big mouth Drew,
The day we went to the zoo.

So the skunk was returned,
And lessons were learned:
In future Mrs Bell will come too,
Next year when we visit the zoo.

Who Watered The Plant?

I grew a little flower,
I grew it outside.
Our cat kept weeing on it
So it withered up and died.

I Fancy...

I fancy Kelly,
She fancies John,
He fancies Jenny,
She fancies Ron.
He fancies Rita,
She fancies Benny,
He fancies Ghita,
She's after Lenny.
He likes Tim -
I know,
We're worried about him!
Tim fancies Tina,
She loves Lee,
They all fancy someone,
But no one fancies me!

Boys And Girls

Boys and girls are so different,
I know that this is true;
We both have different dangly bits
And we use a different loo.
But although we're totally different,
Both of very different kinds,
The problem is not with our bodies,
It's deep within our minds.
Boys and girls will argue,
Both thinking that they're ace;
If boys are born in a cabbage patch
Then girls are from outer space.
They should not be kept together,
Should be separated by a bog,
Just getting together now and then
When they fancy a quick snog.
But I don't want to be separated,
Though I make a lot of noise,
Because I really fancy girls
And I don't fancy boys!

We're Finished (His Story)

It was on the cards,
It had to happen.
You always pestered me,
You wouldn't stop yapping.
You hated my friends,
You hated my sports.
You hated my clothes,
Even hated my shorts.
Nothing can please you,
You were never happy.
The last time you laughed
You'd poohed in your nappy!

We're Finished (Her Story)

Too right it's over,
It could never work.
It was so difficult
Spending time with a jerk.
You loved your mates,
You loved your sports.
You looked such a plonker
In those stupid shorts.
For you I'm not right,
I'm bad for your health.
You don't need my love,
You're in love with yourself!

This Could Be You!

"Mum, can I have a bar of chocolate, please?
Oh, please! Go on, get me one.
Can I? Why not? I want one!
Get me one now! I want one now!
Not later! Not tomorrow!
I want one this minute!
You're making a fool of me!
Don't be so tight!
You're so selfish!
You don't care about me!
You never buy me anything!
I hate you!
I wish I had another mum!
I wish I was never born...
Mum, can I have a bar of chocolate, please?

The Problem With Teachers!

What is wrong with teachers?
Were they ever young?
Do they ever stop moaning?
They're worse than my mum.

Do they know what fun is?
Do they do as they are told?
I think the problem with teachers
Is that they're born very old!

What's In A Name?

We went away with school
On a holiday to France;
We met some foreign students
At a local dance.
They were called:
Claude, Sasha, Jules, Pierre,
Marco, Nina, Margot, Hilaire.
But me, Lez, Tez, Baz, Gaz,
Maz, Shaz, Gez, and Kaz
Thought it such a shame
That they had been lumbered
With such strange names.

Wilf's Poem To His Little Brother

When I was young
I was just like you,
I enjoyed simple things,
Got told what to do.

When I was young
I didn't know
The wonders of the world,
For that I had to grow.

When I was young
The knowledge that I had
Was not very reliable;
I got it from my dad.

But now that I'm older
My life is a scream,
And you will be like me
When you become thirteen.

Can You Smell Something?

No matter how much I wash
I still smell of bad sweat.
I put on loads of deodorant
But my armpits soon get wet.

My feet they smell so cheesy,
My trainers smell of death,
And every time I burp
There's a strange smell on my breath.

The doctor said it's my hormones,
It's very common at my age.
I hope they change real soon,
I smell worse than my hamster's cage!

I Love Lisa

I have told all my friends
That I love Lisa;
I think that she knows,
She's a little teaser.
She brushes past me
And gives me a smile;
My legs then go funny,
I can't walk for a while.

I know she has a boyfriend,
But she'll soon get rid of him
When I phone and tell her
That he's seeing a girl called Lyn.
Don't think I'm being nasty,
I think he's a nice guy,
But he will soon be history
When she hears my little white lie.
I know that I love her,
She's so tall and slim
And I could make her so happy
If she would get rid of him.
And when we are together
We will walk her pet dog;
I can't wait for that day
Because I'm dying for a snog!
People say that I am dreaming,
She would never go out with me;
But I say it doesn't matter
That I'm thirteen, she's twenty three.

Playing Out

There was a girl called Fanny,
There was a boy called Willy;
Every night when Willy played out
Fanny would act so silly.

The Wedding

My cousin is getting married
And everyone's going mad
Because her future husband
Is older than her dad.
I don't know what's the problem,
I don't know why they're bothered.
They should be glad to get rid of her,
I think that she's really horrid.

Young Man From Melrose

There was a young man from Melrose,
Who was trying to touch his toes,
But as he bent his knees
He let out a big sneeze
And snot shot out of his nose.

Scary Hairy Mary!

Something's wrong! My body's changing
And all my emotions are in a whirl;
I've started growing hair on my face
Which isn't right because I'm a girl!

Mum says not to worry, she was the same,
But it's much worse than I feared;
The other day we visited my grandma
And I noticed that she had a beard!

Mum said that all the girls in our family
Tend to grow up a bit hairy,
But with a beard and moustache
I'm sure boys will find me scary!

I'm Sorry, But...

I wanted to finish with my girlfriend
But I didn't know what to say.
Should I say, "It's not working,"
Or just tell her to go away?

I know she will soon get over it,
There are plenty more fish in the sea,
But she'll have to fish a very long time
To catch one as good as me.

Should I tell her I still love her?
That my heart is not full of hate?
And she will still be seeing me
'Cos I'm going out with her best mate!

I was thinking over these problems,
I'm not the type to scoff,
When my girlfriend phoned me up
To tell me to just sod off!

Roller-Coaster Ride

I want to go on the roller-coaster!
I want to go on the roller-coaster!
I want to go on the roller-coaster!

Oh, no!
Oh, no!
Oh, no!

I want to get off the roller-coaster!
I want to get off the roller-coaster!
I want to get off the roller-coaster!

Young Girl From Leeming

There was a young girl from Leeming
Who liked the sport of swimming,
But while doing the breaststroke
Her new bra strap broke
And set the boys off grinning.

How Could You?

I used to have a friend,
Dan was his name.
I no longer see him
Because he's not the same.

He didn't do anything wrong,
It was something that he said.
I couldn't believe my ears,
He must have lost his head!

We were having a conversation
About the way that we feel,
And all the girls we fancy
And if vampires are real.

He then dropped his bombshell,
He wasn't making fun.
He's turned into a weirdo,
He said he fancied my mum!

What Did You Learn?

What did you learn at school today?
What did you see? What did the teacher say?
Was it interesting? Was it worth it?
Did you learn anything? Not even a little bit?
If the answer's 'no' to most of these questions
Why not try listening in some of your lessons?
I know they can be boring, sometimes slow,
But believe me, there *are* things you don't know.

Man From Kentucky

There was a young man from Kentucky,
Who thought himself so lucky.
He once tried for a kiss
With a surly young miss
And was slapped for being mucky.

It's Super!

I am a super-hero!
I have a special power.
Mum says with a face like mine
I could turn milk sour.

Punk Dad

My dad was a singer
In a punk rock band;
They couldn't play a note
But were the best in the land.
They all had strange names
No one would forget:
Rat, Slasher, Baz,
Dad was known as Vomit.
He toured the country
With a pin through his nose,
Bright green spiky hair
And tears in his clothes.
He talks of many groups
Off which I've never heard:
The Stranglers, Pistols, Undertones;
Dad's band were the Dead Bird.
They never had a wash,
Dad says that he stank,
But things are so different now
He's the manager of a bank.

An Excuse For Being Late

I bought a new alarm clock,
It played a silly tune,
Every time it set off
It echoed around my room.

I set it for seven a.m.
To get up nice and early,
But the stupid thing set off
That night at eight thirty.

Then off again at ten,
At twelve went off once more,
Started buzzing at half past three
Then set on fire at four.

By now I was so tired
I couldn't stop yawning,
I fell to sleep at half past six,
That's why I'm late this morning.

What Are You Looking At?

I can see you
From my wheelchair,
I watch you pass.
I watch you stare,
I know what you think
As you walk on.
Well my legs don't work
But my brain's pumping iron.
I don't want your pity,
I know what you feel.
Well, I'm just like you
But I move by wheel.
Do I look so strange?
Well, I really don't care.
Either you get to know me
Or go elsewhere and stare.

What We Did On Our Holiday!

We got up late.
Rushed out to the taxi,
Mum and dad were irate.

Got to the airport.
Dad rushed to check in,
Mum had bags to sort.

We caught our flight.
Dad fell asleep,
Mum had air fright.

Arrived ten a.m. on the dot.
Two weeks in sunny Greece,
Boy was it hot!

Arrived at the hotel.
Mum not very happy,
Room had a strange smell.

Mum started a list:
"Things that are not right.
I'll complain about this."

Visited some tourist sights.
Piles of old rubble,
Tavernas with lights.

I acted quite slack.
Forgot the sun cream,
Skin peeled off my back.

Met a new best friend.
Had a water fight,
Drove parents round the bend.

We all went to the disco.
I can't dance
But I had a go.

Mum acted so strange.
She embarrassed my dad,
That made a change.

She'd drunk too much wine.
Flashed her knickers at Costas,
He had a good time.

Met a girl called Jane.
She was fun at first,
But turned out a pain.

We went on a date.
Went to buy a drink,
She started snogging my mate!

Met another girl that night.
She was a good laugh,
She turned out alright.

I later got into a mess.
Drank some thing called Ouzo
Then threw up down her dress.

And so the holiday went on.
We lost our morals
In the blazing Greek sun.

We gave off the wrong signals.
People started to avoid us
Saying we're worse than the Dingles.

Our two weeks were just splendid.
I know if we had stayed longer
Greece would have surrendered.

Ewe Do The Washing!

Mary had a little lamb
Its fleece was as white as snow;
That's because she washed it
In new improved Grade O.

Grade O washing powder
Gives you gleaming sheep;
It also destroys the environment
But it's very cheap.

(Before putting your sheep in the washing
machine, always read the label first.)

Just Look At Her Now!

She was small and skinny
With pigtails in her hair;
She used to be alright
But now I think I like her.

We used to tease her,
Never once caring;
Just look at her now,
I can't stop staring!

She looks so good,
Ties my belly in knots;
She's developed busters,
I've developed spots.

I wish I'd been nice,
Taken more care;
She used to be alright,
Now I think I like her.

The Easter Bunny

There is a rabbit
Called the Easter bunny,
As he hops around
People think him funny.

It's not his ears
Or his long thin legs,
It's the fact that a rabbit
Lays chocolate eggs.

Flying

I'm so scared of flying,
I know it's so absurd,
But if man was meant to fly
He'd have wings like a bird.

Jack's Beans Talk

Jack had a cow to sell
Because he was very poor,
He took it to the market,
He'd sell it there for sure.
But he came across a man
Who told him of his schemes,
He took the cow off his hands
For a few lousy beans.
Now I don't know about you,
But you'd think he'd find it funny
Parting with his mother's cow
And not getting any money.
So if you're out there, Jack,
I have an old dustbin lid,
If you want to give me a call
It's yours for a hundred quid!

Georgie Pongy

Georgie Porgie pudding and pie,
Kissed the girls and made them cry;
To the girls it was the kiss of death,
Georgie Porgie had such bad breath!

I Cannot Rhyme!

My dad is called Gez,
My mum is called Carol,
My mum has a bum
The size of a barrel.
Well that last statement
Wasn't at all true,
I just can't rhyme Carol!
Can you?

Talking Your Language?

Do your parents talk your language?
Do they understand your words?
Do they know what's hip and trendy?
Or are they both a couple of nerds?

Do your parents seem so distant?
Do they seem so very cold?
Do they sometimes try to act young?
Do they know they're very old?

Do they let you have your freedom?
Or would they like you in a cage?
Try sometimes to understand them,
They're from a very different age.

High Up In A Tree

A monkey and an elephant
Were sat high up in a tree.
"I'm Rod," said the elephant,
"Why do you keep staring at me?"
The monkey said, "I'm so sorry,
But I just found it a bit odd."
They both looked down from the tree.
"I've never met an elephant called Rod!"

When I Was A Lad!

My dad always says,
"When I was a lad!"
This drives me barmy,
It drives me mad!
He could go out swimming,
Get crisps and a coffee
And have his bus fare home
All for 10p!
He had no videos
Nor any computer games;
He had LPs not CDs
And no trainers with names.
I've told dad to wake up,
Try to have some fun,
It's time he realised
It's a new millennium.

Who Am I?

Who is my mother's, brother's, sister's, father's,
Wife's, daughters, husband's, son?
Who am I?

Answer: me!

59

Woke Up This Morning

I woke up this morning,
I was late for school,
I had stayed up late
Like a stupid fool.
Walked to the bathroom,
In the cabinet started groping
For my tooth brush and pastes,
My eyes were barely open.
I'd no sooner started brushing
When I let out a scream,
I wasn't using toothpaste
But some spot-removing cream!

Moo, Moo Black Sheep

Baa, baa, black sheep,
Have you any wool?
No, sir! No, sir!
I happen to be a bull!

Dangerous Technology

Today we had technology
Which left me feeling numb;
Every time I used a hammer
I missed and hit my thumb.

My thumb-nail is now black,
It is really such a mess;
After watching me use a hammer
Teacher said to give the band-saw a miss!

Letting Off Steam

Today I had a sauna,
I thought I would die,
The room filled with steam,
The temperature was too high.
After sitting all alone
I couldn't take it any more,
I had to take my jumper off
Before I collapsed on the floor.

A Big Misnake!

Big wild man Tarzan
Swung through the trees
Making such silly noises,
Flashing his bony knees.
It didn't take very long
For him to see his mistake,
He wasn't holding on to a rope
He was holding a very big snake!

What Part Of A Chicken Is...?

I like eating take away chicken,
We buy it in big buckets.
I've seen their legs, breast, wings,
But where the heck's their nuggets?

The More Mature Wilf

Mum says that I should act mature
And stop acting so wild,
Stop running around the house
Because I'm no longer a small child.

I think she should loosen up,
Why should I have to please?
Anyway, being more mature
Makes me sound like a cheese.

Ron

There was a young man called Ron,
Who had an exploding bum.
He let out a big fart,
Tore his trousers apart
And said, "Look what I've done!"

The Eye Test

I

Went to have

Both my eyes

Tested today.

I'm glad to say
They were both okay.

Ask A Snowman For Nothing

A snowman will never love you,
Or be your friend forever.
He won't promise you a favour
Because he thinks he's clever.

A snowman will never marry,
He would rather live in the street.
He will never commit himself
Because a snowman always gets cold feet.

How To Treat A Girl (His Story)

Just act so cool,
Don't say much,
If they fall in love,
Kick them into touch.

How To Treat A Boy (Her Story)

When they start to brag
Don't listen to what is said,
Treat them like a puppy:
When good, pat on head.

Simple Simon

Simple Simon met a pie man
On the way to his dad's.
Said Simple Simon to the pie man,
"Excuse me, do you sell kebabs?"

Red Hot Stuff

It was late the other night,
I went and bought a curry,
The next morning when I awoke
I needed the toilet in a hurry.
Just what do they put in them
That makes you feel so rotten?
To eat them you need a concrete mouth
And a reinforced fire-proof bottom.

Tweety Bird

Oh, little bird, outside my window
With your constant cheep, cheep,
**Clear off and annoy someone else,
I'm trying to get some piggin' sleep!**

Benny's Bunny

Benny's bunny bit a bit
Off Betty's bunny's botty.
Betty bawled at Benny
Believing Benny had bought
A botty-biting barmy bunny.

Crazy Maisie

Crazy Maisie scares all the boys
As she runs around acting daft,
Tucking her skirt in her knickers
Because she thinks it's a good laugh.

Crazy Maisie she fancies a boy,
His name is little Drew.
He's scared, won't go out alone,
But doesn't know what to do.

Crazy Maisie got kicked out of school
For hitting the teacher with her bag.
She drank the water from the fish tank,
She thought that school was just a drag.

Crazy Maisie is not that bad
She's just wild and free.
The thing I like most about Maisie
Is that she doesn't fancy me!

A Load Of Old Rubbish!

Every week at eight a.m.
The dustbin men call,
They sneak up to our house
Not making a sound at all.

They then empty our bin,
Not spilling a single drop,
And if they ever did
They would be sure to clean it up.

Do you think this is true?
Or could this be a lie?
Well if you believe that rubbish
You'll believe that pigs can fly.

Cross My Heart

I won't cross my heart
And hope to die
If I were to tell a lie.

But I will hop about
And scream and shout
If I was ever found out.

Never Kiss My Dog

Never kiss my dog
Whatever you do,
I've just seen him in the garden
Eating his own pooh!

Talking Of Pets

(Her Pet)
I like riding my horse,
She looks at me saying, "Neigh!"
She's so proud and strong
That I could ride her all day.

(His Pet)
I don't like riding my dog
He's a small skinny little woof,
And if I tried to sit on him
He'd bite my leg and run off!

Tough Man

My boyfriend he plays rugby
And thinks he's really tough,
Thirteen boys with an odd shaped ball
All acting very rough.

He's bigger than other boys are,
Has a gang called Devils Riders,
But I think he's a big soft wimp
Because I know he's scared of spiders.

The Bike Ride

I'm going on a bike ride,
I'm going with my mate,
We're going in the morning
And we won't be back till late.

We do this every week
But no matter where we roam,
We always end up lost
And can't find our way home.

So we're going to take a map
To show just where we are,
But I know we'll end up phoning dad
To come and pick us up in the car.

When Is A Fly Not A Fly?

You may think this is sad,
You may think I'm all talk,
But I think a fly without wings
Should be called a walk.

What Is True Love?
(Her Story)

Love is mounds of chocolate,
Piled so very high,
Love is a very sad film
Where the hero makes you cry.
Love is that little gift
He bought for your birthday,
Love is the peace and quiet
You have when he's gone away.

What Is True Love?
(His Story)

Love is a football match,
Watching your favourite team,
Love is lying in bed
Finishing a brilliant dream.
Love is messing about,
Having a real good time,
Love is being with a girlfriend,
But I'm talking about mine.

Chitty, Chitty, Oh, No!

My dad has bought a car,
I think he's dropped a clanger,
He thinks it's a bargain,
I think it's a banger.

It can only crawl up big hills
With smoke belching from the back,
And every time he starts it up
It lets out an almighty crack.

I think it's so embarrassing,
He thinks it's so cool,
I've told him never to
Pick me up from school.

Big Words

Why do some people
Use very big words?
Are they clever?
Are they nerds?
I think big words
Can cause irritation.
I think it's just
Floccipaucinihilipilification.

To Pee Or Not To Pee

There was once a man
Called Harry Shakespeare
Who lived quite a while back,
He'd have said in yesteryear.

Now Harry was a writer,
He worked so very hard,
Though no one liked his prose
He thought himself a bard.

His writing needed some help
So he had worked out a plan:
"To change my style of writing
I need to call in a P. R. man."

Now this P. R. man was a creep
And crawling was his skill,
He said, "Lose the name dear,
"I think we'll call you Will."

So Harry changed his name,
A new moniker to carry,
He was now William Shakespeare,
Or the artist formally known as Harry.

Then he changed his work,
He'd written about his slipped disk
And named it *Roll Me Over Juliet,*
But the creep said it was a risk.

"You need to write of love."
Will said, "This is my best yet.
"It's about a girl I used to date,
"I have called it *Pam Lett.*"

"No!" screamed the creep.
"We need more murder and intrigue."
So Will hid his play *The King That Leered*
And wrote something good to read.

Will wrote all new stories,
And some of his titles were altered,
With this came new-found fame
Which the P. R. man exploited.

But Will still liked his old work,
He thought it was his best,
Though his most favourite line he'd written
Was never put to the test.

It had come to him in a flash:
He was out riding when,
Suddenly needing a toilet,
He rode up to an inn.

He thought, "Should I go now
And set my bladder free,
Or ride on to the next inn.
Oh, to pee or not to pee!"

Who Are You Calling Four Eyes?

Because I wear glasses
Some people call me four eyes,
Just how much this hurts
I don't think they realise.

One day they will regret it
And be full of remorse,
When they see the size of me
When I finish my body-building course!

Never Try This!

When Wilf was little
He had worried his mum,
He came back from school
With blue lips and gums.

His mum rushed him to the doctors'
Saying, "Doctor, what do you think?"
The doctor replied, "I think you shouldn't
Suck a biro when it's leaking ink!"

Beware Of This Man

There's a man standing
At the school gates,
Giving little parcels
To the children he hates.
He's everyone's friend,
He's a lot of fun,
But inside his pocket
He may carry a gun.
Inside his little parcels
Are powders and pills,
He says, "Just try it,
"It will give you thrills."
There's a man standing
At the school gates,
Giving little parcels
To the children he hates.
They make you feel strong,
They make you feel fast,
They make you feel good
But the feeling won't last.
Soon your body wants more,
You cannot break free,
Your man will supply you
But he now charges a fee.

There's a man standing
At the school gates,
Selling little parcels to
The children he hates.
You now wish you'd never
Tried his strange mixes,
But you're caught in his hold
And you need your fixes.
You're now spotty and pale,
Your body's getting thin,
But you had been told
To keep away from him.
There's a man standing
At the school gates,
Selling little parcels to
The children he hates.
You now need more money
So you steal and you lie,
Nothing is more important
Than you getting your high.
Your parents are worried,
But what do they know?
They're old and stupid
But they won't let you go.

There's a man standing
At the school gates,
Selling little parcels
To the children he hates.
The man doesn't care
Just how deep you are in it,
There are many more fools -
One born every minute.
So listen to warnings,
Don't be so brash,
Your parents want you healthy,
The man wants your cash.
There's a man standing
At the school gates,
He's the type of person
That everyone hates.